365

LOOK good ♥
feel good TiPS

First published by Parragon in 2012

Parragon
Chartist House
15–17 Trim Street
Bath BA1 1HA, UK

www.parragon.com

Copyright © Parragon Books Ltd 2012
Produced by Tall Tree Ltd
Illustrations by Caroline Watson

All photos shutterstock.com, except 67 Graça Victoria/Dreamstime.com, 301 nicepictures/shutterstock.com

ISBN 978-1-78186-300-8

Printed in China

365

LOOK good &
feel good TIPS

PaRragon

Bath · New York · Singapore · Hong Kong · Cologne · Delhi · Melbourne

contents

blemish care ♥ oily skin ♥ dry skin
♥ sun protection ♥ smell good ♥
squeaky-clean hair ♥ detangle hair
♥ floss and brush ♥ look after your
nails ♥ hair removal ♥ banish shine
♥ sun-kissed look ♥ hide cellulite ♥
clean teeth ♥ defuzz

Introduction

Makeup, flattering clothes, and a great hairstyle can make you look groomed to perfection and beautiful. But what's happening on the inside of your body is even more important—if you feel healthy, you'll look good, too.

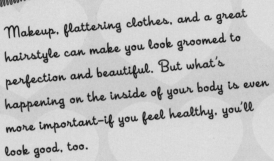

Taking care of your body is not an easy task! Apart from the obvious steps to good hygiene, such as bathing and showering regularly, using deodorant, and keeping your teeth and eyes healthy, it means following a simple grooming regime. This includes looking after your skin, hair, hands, and feet.

To be as healthy as possible, you also need to eat the right amounts of the right kinds of food and drink enough liquid, especially water. Getting regular exercise is also really important. Not only does it keep you in shape physically, it also helps you mentally. And if at the end of the day you're exhausted, a good night's sleep will keep you in good shape, too. If you don't sleep well, it will affect your diet, stress levels, and day-to-day functioning.

With a healthy tip for each day of the year, there is so much information in this book that keeping healthy—and feeling great for it—will become a part of your everyday life.

Chapter 1

beauty

1

Don't do it

Don't squeeze your pimples—you'll only make them redder, and you could cause scarring.

If you have acne, eat foods that are rich in vitamin A, such as melons, spinach, and broccoli.

eat your greens

Under scrub

Oily doesn't mean dirty! If you have oily skin don't overscrub it to get it clean–it could make the problem worse.

Don't dry out

For dry skin, make sure you eat foods rich in essential fatty acids, such as salmon, tuna, avocado, and linseed oil.

4

5

Right on

Use the right products for your skin and hair types.

6

Brimming with health

Wear a wide-brimmed hat to protect yourself from the sun.

Part of you

Your freckles are part of you, so embrace them!
If you try to hide them, you'll just look like
you're wearing too much makeup.

8 workout rinse

Rinse your face after a workout to remove sweat, grime, and blemish-causing bacteria.

On the nails

Don't bite! Biting your nails and picking
your cuticles can damage your nail bed.

10

BRUSH UP

Replace your toothbrush at least every three months to ensure squeaky-clean teeth.

Comb out

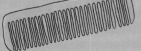

Detangle long hair by holding it in one hand and gently combing it with your other hand.

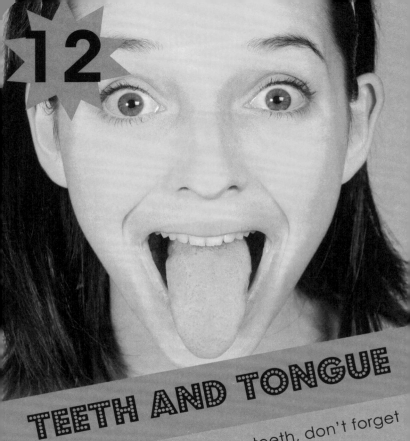

12

TEETH AND TONGUE

When you brush your teeth, don't forget
to brush your tongue, too.

Spot test

Acne?
Try a tinted moisturizer
instead of a foundation.

13

warm, not hot

Warm water is better ...
showering or bathing in
water that's too hot will
dry out your skin.

14

Under the nails

Don't forget to clean under your fingernails—you'd be amazed at what gathers there, especially under long nails.

16 Hair

You wouldn't go outside in the sunshine without a sunscreen on your face, so don't leave your hair bare either. Use hair care products with sunscreen.

clean gums

17

Not just your teeth—brush
below your gum line, too!

18

Alcohol

Avoid mouthwashes that contain alcohol—
they can dry out your mouth.

YEAR ROUND 19

Just because it's winter, don't think you can skip the sun protection—wear sunscreen EVERY DAY.

20 SMILE

Floss and brush! You'll have great-looking teeth and fresh breath if you floss and brush for at least two minutes each day.

Smelling good

Everybody sweats—but by using a deodorant or antiperspirant, you'll smell great and feel great, too.

21

22 Pore law

Pluck your brows just after a shower, when the pores are still open—it's a lot less painful!

23

Keep it clean

Keep your hair clean— dirty, greasy hair is not a good look.

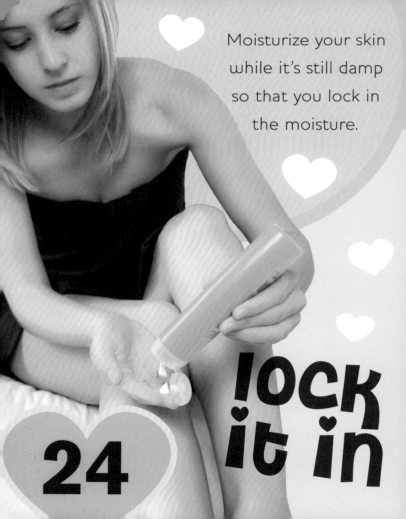

Moisturize your skin
while it's still damp
so that you lock in
the moisture.

lock
it in

24

Exfoliate

Exfoliate your body and face twice a week to get rid of all the dead cells that dull it.

26

Before and after

Even if your makeup has a built-in sunblock, use a proper one after you moisturize and before you put on your makeup.

Fresh and clean

Change your sanitary wear regularly to stay fresh and clean.

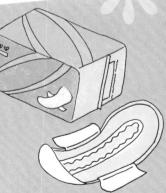

28

can

it!

Make sure you aren't using cosmetics that you've had open for more than a year.

Paste it

To soothe irritation, reduce redness, and dry out pimples, apply a dab of toothpaste to them.

29

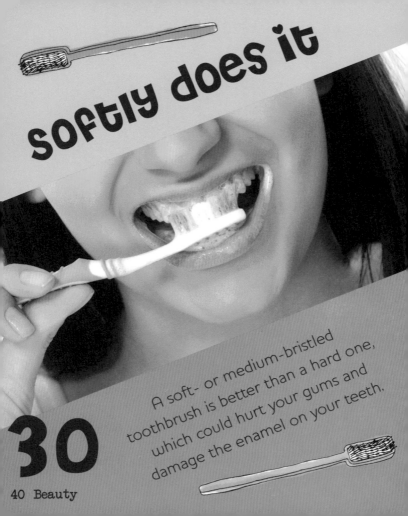

softly does it

A soft- or medium-bristled toothbrush is better than a hard one, which could hurt your gums and damage the enamel on your teeth.

30

40 Beauty

31

Watch the soaps

Don't use the same soap on your face that you use on your body. It could dry out your skin and leave you pimply.

32

Clean-up

Unclean makeup brushes can contain dead skin, product buildup and nasty bacteria. Keep them clean to avoid pimples and infections.

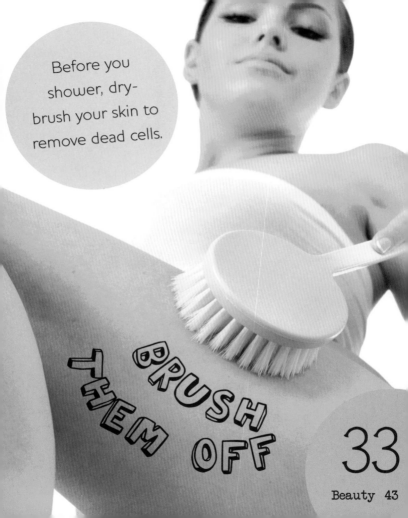

Before you shower, dry-brush your skin to remove dead cells.

BRUSH THEM OFF

33

34

Avoid the sun and hit the bottle! Put self-tanning lotion on before going to bed. When you wake up in the morning, you'll have a sun-kissed look.

hit the bottle

35

Swap it

Wear clean clothes every
day—worn clothes may
look clean, but they aren't.

36

Keep it trim

Healthy, shiny hair looks and feels good—keep your hair in check by having a trim every six to eight weeks.

Pamper time

Pamper yourself with a
manicure or a pedicure—
you'll look great and will
also feel great.

37

38 confidence

Confidence radiates inner beauty, and that's something no amount of makeup can change.

Don't brush, comb! 39

Comb your hair while it is wet to smooth its surface and detangle it.

40

Moisturize your body from top to toe for supersoft skin.

cavity care

Use a fluoride toothpaste to prevent cavities.

41

Beauty 51

42

Banish Dandruff!

Use shampoos with zinc or ketoconazole to get rid of dandruff.

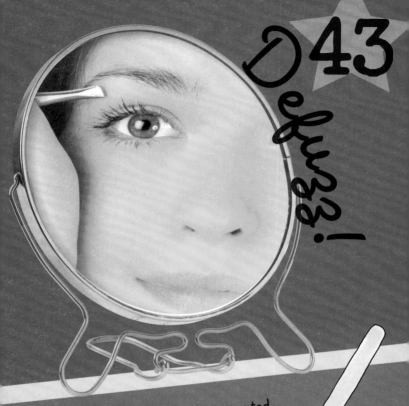

43

Deluxe!

Use tweezers to pluck out unwanted facial hair. Pluck in the same direction in which the hair grows.

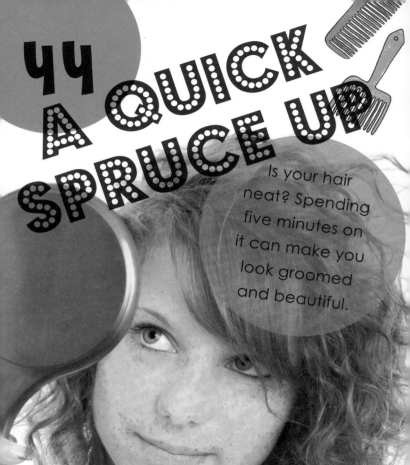

44 A QUICK SPRUCE UP

Is your hair neat? Spending five minutes on it can make you look groomed and beautiful.

sunny with cloudy spells

Wear sunscreen even when it's cloudy—the sun can still burn you.

46

Blot away the shine

Use blotting sheets to get rid of shiny skin during the day.

Swap your locks

A haircut is as good as a vacation—change your hairstyle and feel like a different person!

47

48

Pheeeeeeew!

Banish stinky feet! Sprinkle baby powder in your shoes, change your socks every day, and air your shoes after wearing them.

NAIL IT

49

Your nails will grow faster and stronger if you give them a manicure each week.

50 Makeover magic

Visit a beauty counter and ask them to give you a makeup lesson, then experiment with the look they created when you get home.

51

If you have pimples, keep your hair off your face— even if it's clean!

Face off

Beat the burn

Treat razor burn and ingrown hairs by gently exfoliating the affected area with a washcloth in the shower or bath.

52

smoothie delight

53

Smoothies made of fruit and vegetables are very good for the skin—so why not get blending?

54

I FEEL GOOD

A spritz of perfume can make you feel confident and feminine.

Shave time 55

Shave before you go to bed so that your top layer of skin has a chance to grow back before you go outside again.

If you have brittle nails, avoid hand creams that contain alcohol since these will dry out your nails even more.

No alcohol

56

More is better—you get a closer, cleaner shave when you have three or more blades.

More is
better

58

fake it

Hide cellulite
with fake tan—
it's less noticeable
on dark skin.

DON'T IRRITATE

Don't take a hot shower or bath for a few hours after removing hairs—you could irritate the pores and cause red bumps.

STRETCH THE TRUTH

Stretch marks are part of growing up. Disguise them with makeup or apply a little self-tan to the marked area.

60

Polish off

Nail polish makes you look groomed—take it off as soon as it chips to avoid looking grungy.

61

Germ free!

Don't spread bacteria: Wash your hands before you apply makeup or skin care products.

62

Gently, gently...

If you have acne, use a gentle cleanser in the morning and one with benzoyl peroxide in the evening.

Glasses care

If you wear glasses or sunglasses, keep them clean to avoid clogged pores around your eyes and nose.

64

65

Dry, split

Don't over-
wash your hair,
because overwashing
can cause dryness that
can lead to breakage
and split ends.

Witch for the itch

To prevent soreness, itching, and ingrown hairs, apply witch hazel or tea tree oil to your skin after removing hair.

66

Booster

treat

If your hair is dull,
give it a boost with a
clarifying shampoo.

67

68

HARD AS

NAILS

Use a calcium gel to strengthen brittle nails.

Shave with the grain, then, if you still feel stubble, go against the grain to smooth it out.

A close shave ...

69

Panda
eyes

70 Panda eyes aren't very pretty —take off all your makeup before you go to sleep.

Do the chew

If you can't brush after a meal, chew a sugar-free gum instead.

71

72

stick with it!

Stick to it! Give acne treatments at least two months before you decide if they're working or not.

Ear ear

Never stick a cotton swab into your ear—you could do serious damage. To clean your ears, wipe your outer ear with a washcloth and leave the inner ear alone.

NO SOAP
Don't use soap to shave—it will dry out your skin.

Good hydration

On really hot days, use a hydrating
toner instead of moisturizer.

home
spa

TWICE A DAY

As easy as 1, 2, 3!
Cleanse, tone, and
moisturize your face
and neck twice a day.

76

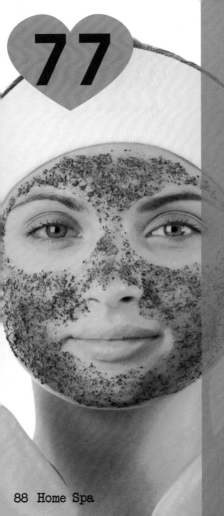

Face time

Make your own face mask by mixing two tablespoons of oatmeal with one tablespoon of honey. Warm the mask in a microwave, then apply to your face. Leave on for about 20 minutes before rinsing off.

78

And relax ...

When you feel stressed and tired, fill your bath with warm water and a couple of drops of lavender oil.

You can keep your skin squeaky clean by cleansing properly.

1. Splash your face with warm water.

2. Apply your cleanser using a circular motion.

squeaky. clean skin

3. Massage your face for about a minute.

4. Rinse with lukewarm water.

5. Rinse again with cooler water, and pat your face dry.

80
Face time

Find the time to apply a face mask once a week.

81
Salt scrub

Make your own salt scrub to exfoliate your skin by mixing olive oil and coarse sea salt.

Brush, then shampoo

For healthy hair, exfoliate your scalp! Get a padded brush, and brush your scalp for at least five minutes before you shampoo.

83

Lie down with your feet on a hot-water bottle and a cold eye mask on your face. Relax for 15 minutes, and afterward, you'll feel relaxed and energized.

hot and cold energy

Paste it

For a gentle hand
and foot exfoliator, mix
two tablespoons of sugar with enough
almond oil to make a paste. Massage
the paste into your hands and feet.
Rinse off and pat dry.

85 Breathe in

Breathing for calm and relaxation. Try this when you get a spare moment to yourself:

1. Close your bedroom door and switch off your cell phone, computer, radio, or anything else that could distract you.

2. Set a timer for five minutes, and find a comfortable place to sit.

3. Close your eyes and focus on your breathing: As you inhale, think about your lungs inflating, your ribs expanding, and the breath moving through your nasal passages. As you exhale, think about your lungs deflating and the breath rushing out of your nasal passages.

4. If your mind starts to wander, calmly say to yourself "breathe" and then turn your attention back to your breath.

breathe out

86

For instant calm, next time you wash your hair, massage your scalp with the pads of your fingertips.

Instant calmer

87

HOME MANICURE

For beautiful, healthy hands and nails, do your own manicure:

1. Remove any old nail polish using a cotton ball and nail polish remover.

2. Shape your nails using an emery board. File each nail from the corner to the center. If you file with a seesaw motion, you'll cause your nails to split.

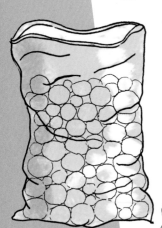

3. Soak your hands in warm, soapy water for a few minutes to clean and soften the cuticles.

4. Use an orange stick to gently push back the cuticles and clean under the edge of each nail.

5. Use a hand-softening scrub to polish and nourish your hands, then rinse it off in clean, warm water and pat your hands dry.

6. Apply a base coat, and when it's dry, your nail polish. When this is dry, give it a second coat of polish.

7. Apply a topcoat to help your color last a little longer and to give your nails a lovely shine.

8. When your nails are completely dry, smother them in moisturizer.

88

hot milk

Milky skin has never
been easier! Steam your face
with hot milk to decongest pores and
leave your skin clear.

100 Home Spa

Lemon aid

To smooth rough skin on your feet, knees, and elbows, cut a lemon in half and rub it over them.

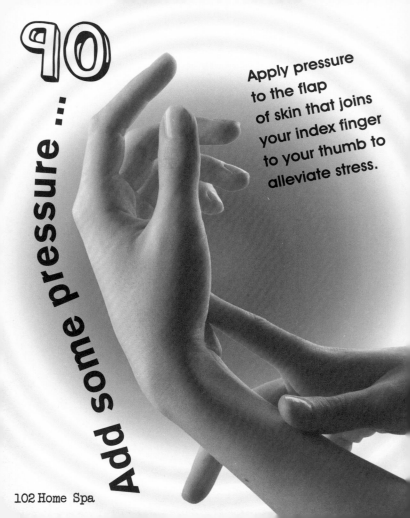

90

Add some pressure ...

Apply pressure to the flap of skin that joins your index finger to your thumb to alleviate stress.

91

To apply moisturizer, start in the center of your face, using your fingers to dab the product on your skin, and gently sweep up and out toward the edge of your face. Don't forget your neck!

Center
start

AND SOAK TO SLEEP

Soaking in a warm bath will relax you and make you sleepy.

92

93

Tasty face

To make a yummy face mask, mix 1/3 cup of cocoa powder, 3 teaspoons of heavy whipping cream, 2 teaspoons of cottage cheese, 1 cup of honey, and 3 teaspoons of oatmeal into a paste. Smooth onto your face, and leave for ten minutes before rinsing off.

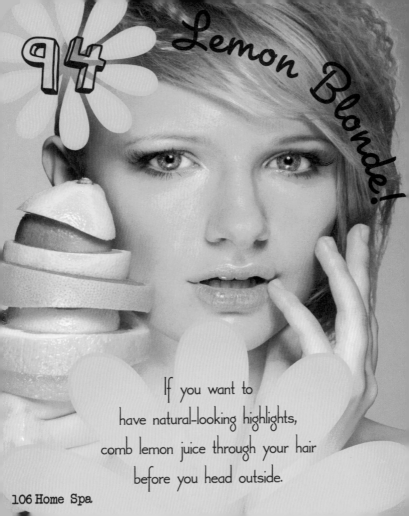

94 Lemon Blonde!

If you want to
have natural-looking highlights,
comb lemon juice through your hair
before you head outside.

95

Don't feel the burn

Pour half a teaspoon of lavender essential oil, half a cup of aloe vera gel, one teaspoon of vitamin E oil, and one teaspoon of apple cider vinegar into a spray bottle. Shake well and spray on your sunburn.

96

Avocado hair masks make great conditioners for dry hair. Make a mask by mashing together half a peeled avocado, an egg, two tablespoons of olive oil, castor oil, and wheat germ. Massage the mixture onto dry hair and leave for half an hour before washing off.

hair mask

spritz and
swim

If you plan on spending your
day in a swimming pool, spritz on
some leave-in conditioner to avoid
damage from chlorine and salt.

Whip it up

To reduce large pores, try this face mask. Whip the whites of two eggs into a light foam. Spread a thin layer of the foam onto your face. Allow the foam to become firm, then simply rinse off.

98

Fix the damage

For very damaged hair, rub warm olive oil into your hair and leave it on overnight.

100 Oats So Smooth

Wrap some oats in a washcloth and tie it closed with a rubber band. Put the "ball" in your bath for smooth, hydrated skin.

You just need honey, Honey

After washing your face, gently apply honey with your hands to your face, lips, and eyelids. After 10 – 20 minutes, rinse off.

nutrition

Papaya Passion

Papaya is not only high in antioxidants and vitamins, but it is also a good food to heal problem skin.

102

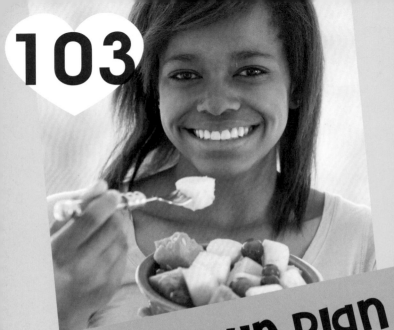

103

Four-hour Plan

Eat something every four hours so that you don't starve yourself from one meal to the next.

H2O TOO

104

Drinking tea, coffee, and sugary drinks can make you dehydrated, so make sure you drink some water, too.

105

healthy Inside

Eat plenty of fiber-rich food, such as whole-grain bread, legumes, and cereals for a healthy digestive system.

TREATS

Everything in moderation! Being healthy doesn't mean giving up your favorite treats—instead, limit them to special occasions.

Nutrition 119

Wait until you have
finished your meal before
deciding whether or
not you're going to have
dessert; skip it
if you feel full.

Desert
the
dessert

Smart snacking

Snack smart by choosing
healthy snacks from
different food groups.

109

BRUSH, BRUSH

If you find your willpower waning, brush your teeth—you won't want to eat right away, and you may just forget about food.

Fruit 'n' veg

Five a day keeps the doctor away—
eat five portions of fruit
and vegetables a day.

110

111

Don't snack

Eating a healthy lunch will stop you snacking later in the day on fatty foods that are low in nutrients.

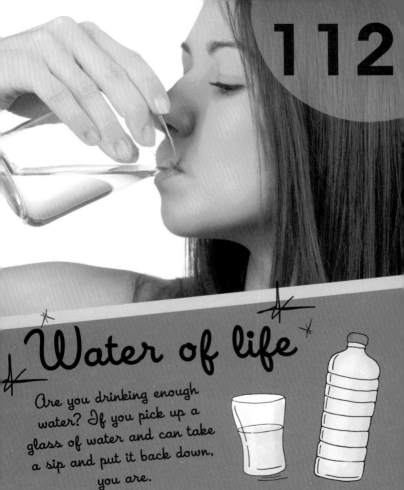

Water of life

Are you drinking enough
water? If you pick up a
glass of water and can take
a sip and put it back down,
you are.

Don't eat too much

113

Avoid a large meal the night before an exam—you'll sleep better after a lighter meal.

HEALTHY HABITS

Do not "go on a diet." Switch to healthier eating habits that you can continue long term.

morning detox

Detox in the morning by having a mug of hot water with a slice of lemon in it before you eat or drink anything else.

116

Ditch the sugar

If you find ditching sweet sodas difficult, go for sugar-free versions.

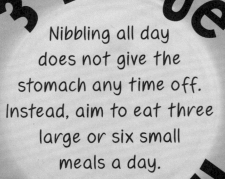

3 Large

Nibbling all day does not give the stomach any time off. Instead, aim to eat three large or six small meals a day.

6 small

117

Try to eat fruit and vegetables that are different colors. That way, you'll be getting a good range of vitamins and minerals.

Red, yellow, green...

119

be label able

Find out more about food so you know what you're eating.

Feed your brain

Feed your brain and aim for three portions of oily fish, such as salmon, a week.

Ditch the
scales

Ditch the scales. Instead, aim for a waist size that is less than half your height (in inches).

121

122

Chew

lips

Help your
digestion by
chewing your
food properly.

satisfied?

Eat until you're satisfied, not stuffed.

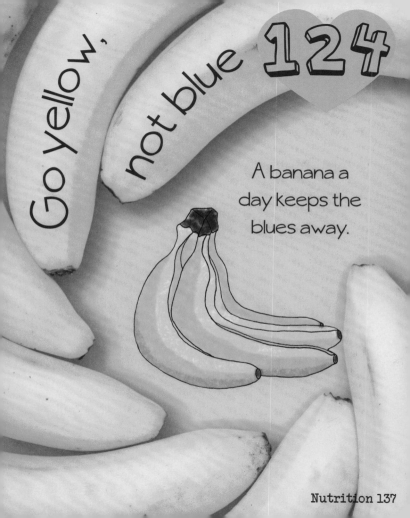

Go yellow, not blue

124

A banana a day keeps the blues away.

SMOOTHIE HEAVEN

Smoothies are easy to make and packed full of nutrients. Put your favorite fruit into a blender—use soft fruits such as strawberries, mangoes, and bananas. Add some yogurt, some milk, or for a treat, some ice cream. Blend until smooth.

125

Half size! If you're going out to eat and the restaurant is known for big portions, ask for a half portion.

126

Don't be afraid to ask

127

get with the green scene

Fight disease by eating broccoli, cabbage, cauliflower, watercress, and arugula three times a week.

128

Easy detox!

For a simple detox, cut out caffeine and eat less sugar, salt, wheat, dairy, meat, and processed foods for a few days.

129

Eat calcium-rich foods, such as dairy products, now to ensure strong bones in the future.

Future plan

I3O

Running on empty

F ||||||||||||||||||||

E

Don't skip a meal:
you'll only reach for
something sugary or
fatty later.

131 Fill up on protein

Eating protein at each meal will keep you fuller for longer.

slow and steady

If you're trying to lose weight and it's not happening fast enough, remember that if you lose weight gradually, you'll be more likely to keep it off.

132

133

Take a multivitamin each day to make sure you get all the vitamins and nutrients you need to support your growing body.

A vitamin a day

Tea for you

Tea, a drink
to cleanse your body
... Drink herbal teas,
including green tea, for
healing energy and
antioxidant power.

134

135

Fill empty space
on your plate
with salad rather
than bread.

Salad days

Water it down

Dilute your fruit juice with water to reduce the calories.

136

137

Avoid strict detoxes
—they can be
especially unhealthy
for teenagers.

Don't be strict

Zzzzzzzzzzzz

Before bedtime, drink a cup of chamomile, anise, or fennel tea to help you sleep.

139

Keep healthy snacks at hand to avoid reaching for unhealthy ones.

Snack attack...

Get stuffed

The 20-minute rule: It takes 20 minutes for you to feel full, so pace yourself so that your meals last at least 20 minutes.

140

141 wrap UP! ♥

Make a nutritious veggie wrap with roasted vegetables and low-fat cheese rolled in a tortilla—even better if the tortilla is whole wheat.

Veggie smoothies are great for detoxing, and they're superrich in nutrients because the veggies are raw.

Silky smooth

143

Berry good!

Berries are not only good for your stomach, they also contain antioxidants that fight cancer and heart disease.

Wonder food!

Watermelon wonder food! This delicious fruit contains lycopene, an antioxidant that fights against cancer.

145

Try this for a great, healthy snack:
- Drain and rinse a can of chickpeas.
- Purée them with a tablespoon of tahini (sesame seed paste), a teaspoon of olive oil, and lemon juice and garlic to taste.
- When the paste is smooth, serve with chopped veggies.

SUPER SNACK

146

Eat regularly to keep your metabolism up to speed.

Round the clock

Easy frozen yogurt

Add some frozen fruit, such as berries, to some fruit-flavored yogurt. Combine in a blender until smooth. Eat immediately.

147

148

Oaty Energy

Oats contain calcium, potassium, magnesium, and vitamins E and B, making them superhealthy. An oaty breakfast will keep your energy levels up and snack cravings down.

NUT CRACKERS

Try some chestnuts—they're the only low-fat nut, and they're high in vitamin C, too.

149

150

french toast

A couple of slices of French toast will set you up nicely for the day:

• Beat together an egg, two tablespoons of milk, and a dash of vanilla extract.

Make starch a part

Try to include
at least one
starchy food
with each of
your main meals.

151

- Soak two slices of bread in the egg
mixture until the egg has been soaked up.
- Fry the bread in a little oil-spray until it's
cooked and crispy.

- Add some blueberries,
if you like, and eat
while warm.

152 Pink Drink

For a refreshing, healthy drink, mix together pineapple, pomegranate, and lemon juice, then dilute it with water.

veggie extras

If you're a vegetarian, you need to make sure you're getting enough iron (found in fortified breakfast cereals, breads, dried fruits, beans, peas, and lentils), B vitamins (found in yeast extracts, soy milk and other soy products), and zinc (found in whole-grain breads and legumes).

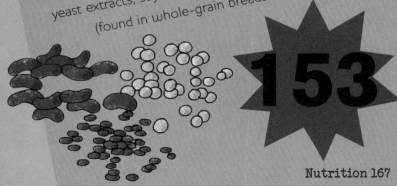

153

154 Fuel up!

Place half a cup of rolled oats in a bowl. Add half a cup to a cup of milk. Microwave on high for two-and-a-half minutes. Add some chopped fruit or nuts. If you don't have a microwave oven, boil the oats and milk on the stove, and leave to simmer for around five minutes.

Don't cut out carbs altogether. Instead, choose good ones (whole grains, brown pasta, and rice) and avoid the bad ones (cakes, candy, and cookies).

Good carb,

bad carb...

155

156 sweet tooth

Try cutting out sugar for two weeks— can you feel a difference?

157

Don't fall for it!

Don't follow a celebrity diet because you think the celebrity looks good—their diets may not be based on solid medical evidence.

158

Big breakfast

Start the morning right by eating a filling and healthy breakfast to set you up for the day.

Mmmmm

If you see or smell a food that looks really tempting—eat it only if you're hungry.

159

160

Two's company

Eat with others—you'll eat less, and chances are, have some fun at the same time!

Tuna melt 161

Place two slices of bread in the toaster. When toasted, spread a mixture of two tablespoons of tuna, mayonnaise, and a handful of grated cheese over the untoasted side of the bread. Cook until the cheese has melted and top with tomatoes, if you like, before serving.

Nearly full

Eat until you're 80 percent full and then stop—you'll be cutting down your calories by 20 percent.

162

The Whole Truth

Whole grains keep you full for longer,
so make sure you eat whole-wheat
products whenever you can.

164

Banana boat

Slice a banana lengthwise. Top with a scoop of low-fat frozen yogurt. Sprinkle with a tablespoon of chopped nuts and some berries.

165

Don't use restaurant portion sizes as a guide— they like to supersize!

SUPERSIZE

53 54 55 56 57 58 59

166

Oranges

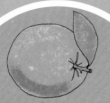

Foods rich in vitamin C help absorb iron.

and lemons

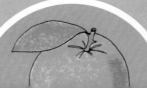

Switch it off!

Eating in front of the television often leads to overeating.

167

168

go green!

Green leafy veggies are great for keeping your eyes healthy.

A-CLASS HAIR

Vitamin supplements that contain vitamin A are great for your hair.

170

chef's salad

You be the chef and decide what to add!

Wash your salad ingredients before you start chopping.

Spot fix

Eat food rich in zinc to prevent
white spots on your nails.

Chop up some lettuce, tomato, and cucumber.

Add any other chopped fruits and veggies, such
as peppers, olives, avocado, and grated carrots.

You can add some cheese or tuna or cooked
chicken, too.

172

POP!

POP!

POP!

Popcorn is full of fiber, and if air popped, it's low-fat ... and delicious!

Food for nails

To avoid dry and brittle nails, eat food that is rich in vitamin A and calcium.

Pit-stop soups

Fill up on healthy soups and salads.

pizza the action

175

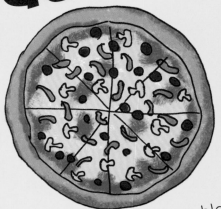

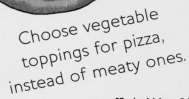

Choose vegetable toppings for pizza, instead of meaty ones.

Nutrition 189

176

Don't eat by the clock, eat when you're hungry.

Time to eat ...

Food Pyramid

Healthy eating means eating from ALL the food groups.

Mash an avocado with a small chopped onion, a chopped tomato, cilantro leaves, and lemon juice. Serve with toasted pita bread.

178

Dip and chip!

Natural is best!
Whenever possible,
eat whole, fresh, and
unprocessed foods.

Au naturel

180 vitamins and greens

If you're worried that you aren't getting enough vitamins in your diet, try taking a vitamin supplement —but don't stop eating all your greens!

Water cycle

Drink plenty of water during your period; it will help to reduce bloating.

82 mega omega

Load up on salmon, sardines, and flaxseed-foods that are high in omega-3, which can help you to concentrate.

Scrambled eggs

- Beat two eggs together with two tablespoons of milk.
- Heat oil spray over medium heat.
- Add the eggs and a handful of grated cheese, such as cheddar.
- As the egg starts to cook, stir it with a wooden spoon to scramble it until it's set.
- Serve on some buttered whole-wheat toast.

183

Snack attack

If you feel starved, you will probably overeat.
Instead, have a snack to keep you going.

get
smart

Smart snack yourself to health! Try some mixed berries and fruit with some low fat yogurt.

185

186

Choc heaven

Chocaholic?
Switch to dark chocolate—it's
richer so you'll eat less, and
it could help to keep
your heart healthy!

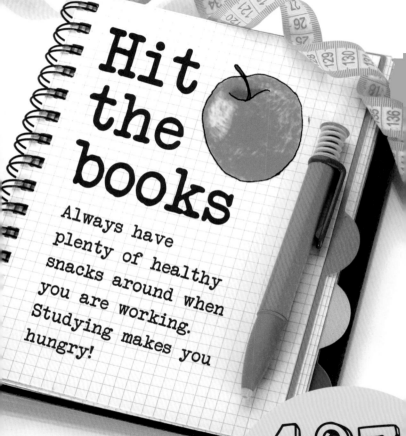

Hit the books

Always have plenty of healthy snacks around when you are working. Studying makes you hungry!

187

muffin top...

188

No more! Eat plenty of vitamin C-rich foods, such as bell peppers and kiwifruit, to reduce fat-storing hormones in your body.

Brittle hair? Eat plenty of legumes, such as kidney beans and lentils.

Lovely
legumes

Don't listen

Lies and more lies! Don't avoid avocados because they're high in fat—they're packed with good fats!

190

Very berry

191

Add berries and apples to foods such as pancakes, waffles, and French toast.

192 SUPER VIT C

For a vitamin C superboost, add a cup of peeled kiwi to a cup of honeydew melon and half a cup of low fat vanilla yogurt. Combine it in a food processor until it's creamy and smooth.

Hungry or dehydrated?

Hungry? Sometimes when you're hungry, you're actually dehydrated. Drink a glass of water and wait 20 minutes to decide.

193

Nutrition 207

194

Healthy bladder

Keep your bladder
healthy by drinking
cranberry juice.

Go nuts!

Eating nuts regularly will keep your hair shiny and healthy.

195

196

Persistence is the key—if you have a bad weight-loss week, put it behind you and start again.

scale it down

Active or bored?

Try to stay active as much as you can with sports and hobbies—it will keep you fit and stop you from getting bored.

197

fruity bowl

Two out of five: Add some fruit and fresh juice to your breakfast, and you've already had two portions of fruit.

Fruit skewers

Chop a mixture of different-colored fruit, such as strawberries, bananas, mangoes, and melon, into chunks. Add some grapes to the mix. Thread the fruit onto skewer sticks and serve with some fresh, fruity yogurt.

199

snack time

Put a full water bottle and a piece of fruit in your bag—you'll stay hydrated and have a healthy snack on board.

200

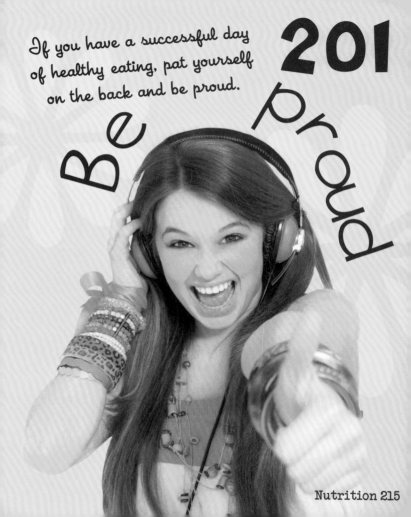

If you have a successful day of healthy eating, pat yourself on the back and be proud.

201

Be proud

before and after

Drink before you exercise, during exercise and after you exercise, to keep hydrated.

203

Steam it

Steam your
veggies rather than
cooking them in
oil and butter.

Iron-rich

If you don't eat enough iron-rich food, you could become anemic. Iron is found in red meat, eggs, poultry, fish, legumes, and fortified cereals.

Drink your greens

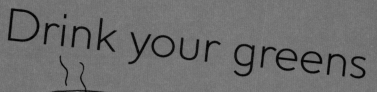

Swap your usual tea for a refreshing green tea when you are feeling tired.

205

206

Choose your role models carefully ... supermodels aren't always superhealthy!

good Role models

Ahhh ...
Mojito

207

For a refreshing drink, add lemon, mint, or frozen strawberries to your water.

208

In the book

Keep a food diary—you'll become more aware of the food you eat.

On your list

Make a list of things to do when you feel like eating but aren't actually hungry.

209

210

Eating out?

Think about sharing a meal with a friend if the portions look large.

211

Don't eat on the run—sit down, relax, and enjoy your meal.

Balanced
diet

There are no good foods or bad foods. All foods can be part of healthy eating. Just watch how much you eat!

212

Try not to arrive at an event hungry—you'll want to eat everything in sight!

The Munchies

Feeling irritable and moody?
Try eating some unsalted
cashews, walnuts,
or hazelnuts.

214 nutter!

By packing your own lunch, you'll know exactly what you're eating, and you can control your portion sizes.

215 Packed lunch

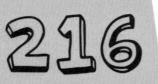

216

Keep fueled

Three to six hours before you exercise, eat a larger meal.

VEGGIE VITAMINS

If you're a vegetarian, you may need to take a vitamin supplement to ensure you're getting everything you need.

217

pizza perfect

218

Pizza is perfect for lunch on the go, but try to keep this as an occasional treat.

219

Lots of veg

For a balanced diet, always
make sure you include
vegetables with your meals.

Popcorn makes a healthy snack. Avoid salty or sugary coatings, though. Plain popcorn is best.

SnackPop

Brown not white

Avoid "white" starch, such as white flour, rice, and pasta.

221

222 Calm down!

Avoid caffeine. Too much tea, coffee, chocolate, and sodas can make you feel nervous or jittery.

Keep it natural

Avoid "diet" foods—they're usually packed with other high-calorie ingredients.

224 Salad sense

Salads can help you to lose weight, but skip the dressing and croutons, and add broiled chicken and fish instead.

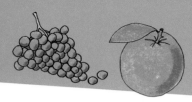

TOUGHEN UP!

When times are tough, load up on vitamin C-rich foods to fight the stress.

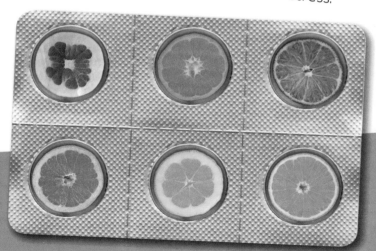

226

Don't eat out of boredom. Find something else to do.

Bored, Bored, Bored ...

Goals!

If you are trying to lose weight, set yourself realistic short-term goals—you'll be motivated when you reach them.

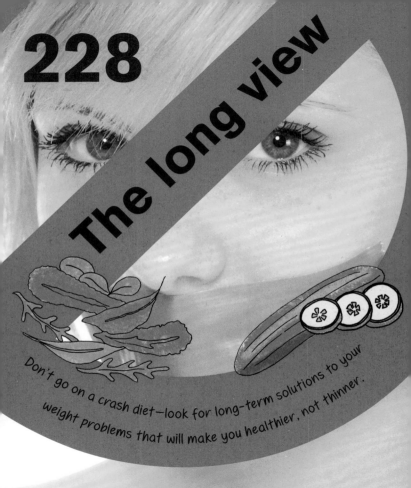

228

The long view

Don't go on a crash diet—look for long-term solutions to your weight problems that will make you healthier, not thinner.

100% free
Craving sweet things?
Try chewing sugar-free gum.

229

230

Piece by piece

Measure out your food rather than eating it straight from a bag or container.

Period 231

gains

Avoid these foods when
you have your period:
Salt: can increase bloating
Caffeine: can cause irritability
Sugar: can make cravings worse.

232

Early eaters

Avoid eating after 7 p.m. so that your body has time to digest the food.

Fork down!

233

If you put your fork down between mouthfuls, you'll eat more slowly.

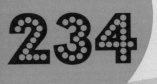

234

Carrots, not cake

Eat veggies that are naturally sweet, such as corn, carrots, sweet potatoes, and squashes, to help curb your craving for sweet things.

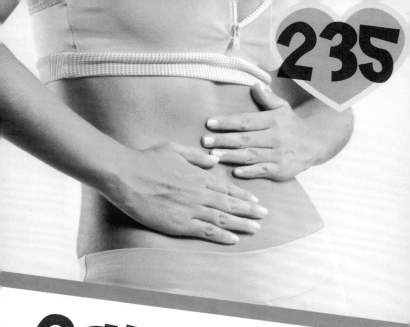

235

eat right

Avoid foods such as broccoli, baked beans, or bran cereal right before exercise. They may cause stomach pains.

Chapter 4

fitness

Push your body

Get sweaty! Workouts keep your body and mind in shape.

236

237

Workout ...

Banish PMS by exercising—exercise can give
you energy and help soothe cramps and bloating.

238

Kickboxing

It's a great way to release stress and learn self-defense moves at the same time.

239 Let's get physical

Keep fit with some 1980s' aerobics videos—they'll make you laugh, too!

Fit
Friends

*It's easier to stick to
a fitness plan if you
exercise with friends.*

240

Little steps

Start small. If you try to do too much exercise too soon, you'll be less likely to stick to your fitness program.

Sit-ups!

Stretch your lower back.
1. Lie on your back and take a few slow, deep breaths.
2. As you exhale, pull your knees to your chest with your hands on your kneecaps.
3. Hug your knees, and rock back and forth and from side to side.

242

Shape Up!

It's never too late to make a change and get your body in shape.

243

Swim, Swim, Swim!

Swimming gives your whole body a workout, and it's easy on your joints.

245

streeeetch!

S-t-r-e-t-c-h yourself to good health. Stretching is good for preventing back problems, and it will relax you, too.

All change ...

Change your exercise
regime every six to eight
weeks—you won't get bored
and neither will your body.

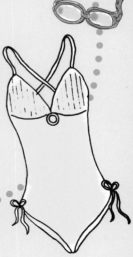

Try to walk 10,000 steps in a day— you can use a pedometer to track your progress.

Walk, walk, walk!

247

248

Hold 'em

Hold your stretches for about 25 seconds. Don't bounce or force yourself into a stretch because you'll do more harm than good.

249 stretch

1. Stand upright with your hands at your sides. Relax your whole body by taking deep breaths.

2. Slowly lower your head until your chin touches your chest. Return to position 1.

3. Keeping your head facing forward, touch your left ear to your left shoulder, and return to position 1.

your neck

4. Now touch your right ear to your right shoulder, and return to position 1.

5. Repeat the three stretches five times.

250

Committing to an exercise program for 30 days will get you in the habit ... and help you to keep at it.

30 days

HAVE FUN

The more fun
you have when
you exercise,
the more you'll
want to stick
to it.

251

Time it right

252

When do you feel most energetic?
That's when you should aim to exercise.

253

Taking your dog for a walk will give you both some exercise.

Walkies!

down in the dumps

Need a boost?
Go for a walk to lift your spirits.

254

sporting a smile

Exercise yourself happy—exercise increases feel-good hormones.

255

Venerdì
Maggio Friday
May   Vendredi
Mai   Freitag
Mai

15

136-230   S. Ubaldo vescovo

8

9

10

11

12

13

14

15

16

17

18

16

Maggio   Sabato
May   Saturday
Mai   Samedi
Mai   Samstag

137-229 S. Pasquale Baylon

17

Maggio
May
Mai
Mai

138-228

Keep-fit calendar

Put your exercise times in your diary,
so you don't plan other things instead.

You can have too much of a good thing. Don't overdo it when it comes to exercise; you could injure yourself or place too much stress on your body.

257

Pace yourself

258

Meet up, not feet up

Instead of chatting to friends on the net or texting them, meet them for a walk in town or around a shopping mall instead.

Eat yourself fitter

If you're underweight and exercise a lot, you'll need to eat more calories to be healthy.

259

X marks the spot!

If you mark an "x" on a calendar every time you exercise, you'll soon see how well you're doing.

260

261 Tag along

If your parents go to the gym, tag
along and get a good workout.

Stretch your sides

● Stand upright
with your feet
shoulder-width
apart. Let your arms
hang by your sides.
● Lift your right arm
over your head,
bending to the left as
far as possible. Hold this
stretch for 10 seconds.
● Return to the starting
position and do the same
stretch but with your left
arm to your right side.

262

263

BOXercise!

Not only will you be fitter, but you'll get rid of any anger or frustration.

The extra mile

If you catch a bus or take a train to get home, get off a stop earlier and walk the rest of the way.

265

FIGHTING FIT

Be a warrior to improve your balance and coordination:

1. Stand tall with your feet together, facing forward.

2. Breathe in, and as you do so, step your left foot back so that your legs are wide apart.

3. Place your hands on your hips, and turn your right leg and foot out by 90 degrees. Your right heel should be directly opposite the inner arch of your left foot.

4. Turn your left leg and foot in by about 45 degrees. Make sure that you feel balanced.

5. Turn your chest to the right. Press your left hip forward to square your hips.

6. Inhale to raise your arms above your head, and bring your palms together.

7. Exhale and bend your right knee to a 90-degree angle. Your knee should be right over your ankle.

8. Drop your tailbone toward the floor, gently lean your head back, and gaze upward at your fingertips. Stretch upward and hold this pose for five breaths.

9. Breathe in and straighten your legs. Lower your arms and bring your legs together, back to where you were in step 1.

266

go by bike

An easy way to exercise: Walk or cycle to and from school or to see your friends.

267

Stretch yourself tired. Stretching before bedtime will relax your body and mind.

TIME FOR BED

268

Walk the dog

Be flexible and strong by doing the downward-facing dog.

1. Get onto your hands and knees.

2. Put your knees directly below your hips and your hands slightly forward of your shoulders.

3. Spread your palms and turn your toes under.

4. Breathe out, lifting your knees away from the floor.

Keeping trim

Do chores, such as vacuuming,
raking, and mowing the lawn,
to keep fit without even
thinking about it.

5. Keep your knees slightly bent and your heels lifted away from the floor.

6. Lengthen your tailbone away from the back of your pelvis, and press it lightly toward the pubic bone. Then lift your sitting bones toward the ceiling.

7. Exhale and push your thighs back and stretch your heels onto or toward the floor.

8. Straighten your knees, but don't lock them.

9. Stretch out your arms, and continue to breathe in and out.

270

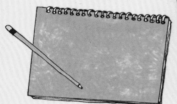

Write it down

When you exercise, write down what you did, how you felt, and how you have improved since your last workout.

Try

The tree pose will help improve balance and concentration.

1. Stand with your feet shoulder-width apart.

2. Shift your weight to your right foot.

3. Lift your left foot to let it rest either against the

the tree

inside of your right ankle (easiest pose), just above the inside of your right knee (more difficult pose), or at the top of your right thigh (most difficult pose).

4. Fix your eyes on something that isn't moving, and slowly begin to lift your arms above your head until your palms meet.

5. Hold the pose for ten breaths, then release and repeat on the other side.

272 Channel your energy

Log on to the net or surf your television channels to see if there's an exercise video or program that grabs your attention.

Burn baby, burn

Build your muscle—if you do some
resistance training, you'll build
muscle, and your body will burn fat
more efficiently.

273

274

MUSCLE POWER

Exercise will give you a healthy glow and help increase muscle tone and definition.

290 Fitness

on your marks!
get set!
go!

275

Enter a race to give
yourself an exercise goal.

Locust pose

For stronger stomach, arm, and leg muscles, and a flexible back, try this pose. Don't do it if you have a back injury.

276

1. Lie on your stomach with your arms palm-side up next to your body. Rest your forehead on the floor.

2. Lift your head.

Keep at it!

Don't stop once
you reach your goal.
Healthy habits should
last a lifetime.

3. Lift your upper torso and arms.

4. Lift your legs, keeping your arms parallel
to the floor, so that you are resting on your
stomach and lower ribs. Stay in this position
for about a minute.

If you're stuck at the same weight and still want to lose a little, trick your body by changing your routine.

For your next trick

278

279

Change the record

Shuffle some songs when you exercise—it will keep you motivated.

TUM 'N' BUM

280

Squats can tone your thighs and bottom, and they're easy to do:

- Stand tall with your feet a little apart and a chair behind you.
- Put your arms straight out in front of you.
- Slowly start to sit down, but stop just before your bottom touches the chair.
- Slowly start to straighten back into your starting position.
- Repeat this at least 15 times.

Red-faced

281

Don't use being embarrassed as an excuse not to exercise. Everyone has to start somewhere.

282

Don't exercise the same group of muscles two days in a row —muscles need time to repair themselves.

Focus groups

Orange-peel skin?

283

Cellulite? The best way to deal with it is to lose any excess weight by eating properly and combining aerobic exercise with strength training.

284

TV winners

Kill two birds with one stone! If you're watching TV, do some sit-ups or push-ups during the commercials.

300 Fitness

Dancing machine

285

Don't like
playing sports?
Do a dance class
to keep fit!

Exercise Express

Quick toning? Do some push-ups—they'll work your arms, chest, stomach, and bum!

Breathe to relax

Sit in a comfortable place and picture one of your favorite things. Now breathe in and hold your breath for a count of one before breathing out again, slowly to a count of ten. Repeat this five times.

287

Fitness 303

288

Keep Busy!

Get active during the day —it will help you to sleep.

Exercise even if you feel tired—
you'll have more energy in the long run.

Breathless

Don't lie on your bed listening to music—put on your headphones and go for a walk.

keep on moving

290

291

On the go

If you're meeting your friends at a shopping mall, instead of sitting down and having coffee, get a takeout cup and walk around.

292

1. Stand up straight.

2. Place feet hip-distance apart.

3. Make sure toes are pointing forward.

4. With your right foot, take a large step backward, creating a lunge position.

Lunge!

5. Your entire body should be in proper alignment, with your ears, shoulders, and hips forming a straight line.

6. Feel the stretch in your right upper calf and lower calf.

7. Breathe in through your nose, and breathe out through your mouth, as you complete the stretch.

8. Hold this stretch for 30 seconds.

9. Repeat on the opposite side.

chest stretch

1. Stand up straight, with knees slightly bent and your feet hip-width apart.

2. Point your toes forwards and keep your shoulders straight.

3. Put your arms behind your back.

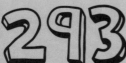

293

Up the stairs

Move it! Climb the stairs instead of taking the elevator or escalator.

4. Clasp your hands together, extending your arms behind your back, and hold this position.

5. Feel the stretch in your chest.

6. Breathe in through your nose and out through your mouth. Hold the stretch for 30 seconds.

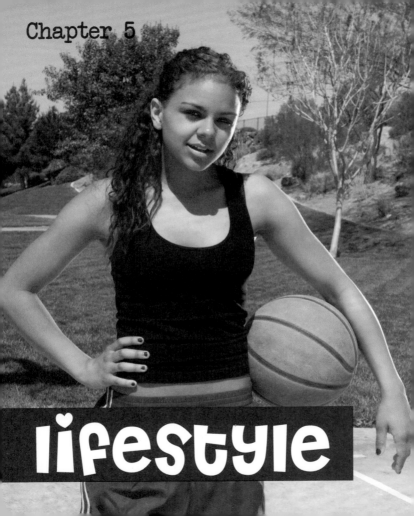

Chapter 5

lifestyle

Carrying a heavy handbag on your shoulder can throw your body off balance.

Lighten the load

295

Keep it bright

Don't study or work in dim light ... use a desk lamp for healthier eyes.

296

Be creative!

Develop your
creative talents—
write poetry or music,
or try your hand at
painting or pottery.

298

Be a yogi! Yoga relaxes the body and helps you feel less stressed.

Breathe in breathe out

Good night
sleep tight

Sleep is vital to being healthy—
make sure you get eight to ten
hours to function properly.

299

Take a break

Don't sit for longer than two hours in front of a computer without taking a break.

300

Turn off the radio when you eat—if a song with a fast beat is playing, you'll eat quicker.

Slow it down

Laugh out loud!

302

320 Lifestyle

Laugh a lot! Laughing strengthens your stomach muscles and relaxes you.

303

Mirror, mirror

Look at yourself in the mirror and say, "I am beautiful." The more you do it, the more you'll believe it, and the more confident you'll be.

Lifestyle 321

Keep it clean

Wash your hands regularly, especially after:
1. Preparing food.
2. Using the toilet or changing a child's diaper.
3. Touching an animal or animal toys, leashes, or waste.
4. Blowing your nose; coughing or sneezing into your hands.
5. Treating wounds or caring for a sick or injured person.
6. Handling garbage, household or garden chemicals, or anything that could be contaminated—such as a cleaning cloth or soiled shoes.
7. And whenever they look dirty.

304

305

Smoke-free

Don't smoke.
Apart from
destroying your
lungs, smoking
damages your
skin and can
cause wrinkles.

Lifestyle 323

306

Friendly advice

A friend in need ... if you can't see any positives in a situation, ask a trusted friend for his or her opinion

307

sunny d·light

Aim to get around 10 to 15 minutes of sunlight a day. It will help fight depression and give you enough vitamin D to keep healthy.

308

Enjoy yourself

You can't change the past or predict the future, so live in the present and enjoy yourself.

309

small CHANGES

Rome wasn't built in a day. Changing your entire diet and exercise program overnight can be hard. Start with small changes and go from there.

check yourself

Examine your breasts for any unusual lumps and bumps every month in the week after your period.

311

Have a siesta

If you're stressed, chances are you haven't slept well, so have a short afternoon nap to perk up.

312

Healthy mind

● ● ● ● ● ● ● ● ● ● ● ● ●

Lovely lavender ... when you feel stressed, put some lavender oil on a tissue and smell it for instant calm.

330 Lifestyle

Stick to a 313
routine

Try to go to bed
and wake up at the same
time every day to ensure
a good night's rest.

314

Wear cotton —it absorbs sweat better so you'll feel cooler.

Keep hygienic

Put the brakes on

If you find your mind racing when you should be sleeping, get out of bed and sit in a chair in the dark until it stops racing, then get back into bed.

316

Stress buster

1. Sit with one hand on your stomach.

2. Close your mouth and relax your jaw.

3. Breathe in through your nose, and allow your stomach to expand.

4. Breathe out slowly, allowing your stomach to flatten.

5. Repeat this five times to feel focused and calmer.

All four corners!

317

If you can't sleep, look at something with four corners. Starting at the top left-hand corner, breathe in for a count of four, and out for a count of four. Repeat this for each corner.

318

To keep your spirits up, include at least one thing each day that you enjoy.

FUN EACH DAY

Can't sleep?

Make yourself
a cup of
hot milk.

319

320

Keep your eyes protected by wearing sunglasses that guard against the sun's harmful rays.

wear shades

ban nasty bugs

Keep your bed linen and bedroom clean to avoid nasty bacteria spreading.

322

If you can't sleep, try telling each part of your body, one at a time, to go to sleep. Start at the top of your head and end at the tips of your toes.

ONE AT A TIME

Get measured! Make sure that you're wearing the right size bra to avoid damaging your breasts.

measured

Get

323

Lifestyle 341

Keep covered

Even if your sunscreen says it's waterproof, reapply it after swimming.

Wide Awake

325

If you can't sleep at night, don't watch TV or surf the net-they will keep you awake.

326 another level

To avoid eye strain, make sure your eyes are level with the top of your computer monitor.

Don't burn

Seek shade—especially when the sun
is at its hottest between 10 a.m. and 4 p.m.

328

Know your shape

Choose styles that compliment your assets and hid your imperfections.

Find a happy song that you can sing to yourself when you're feeling a little down.

don't worry, be happy 329

330

Write it down ...

Keep a notebook next to your bed: if something is playing on your mind while you're trying to sleep, write it down, then put the notebook away until the morning..

1, 2, 3 Blink

When using computers, watching television, and using electronic reading devices, blink often, to prevent dry eyes.

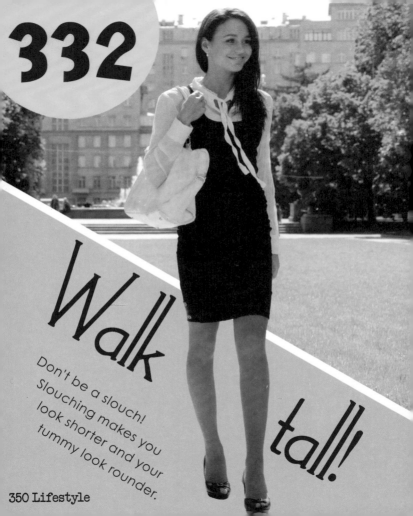

332

Walk

tall!

Don't be a slouch!
Slouching makes you
look shorter and your
tummy look rounder.

333

Done and dusted!

If you're battling to sleep, picture a chalkboard. Imagine writing down the things that are bothering you on the board. Then imagine rubbing them off the board with an eraser.

334

Be yourself

Don't make changes to keep other people happy—make them for yourself.

Eye cleaning

If you wake up with a gooey eye, mix a teaspoon of baking soda in hot water, wait for it to cool, and cleanse your eye with it.

336

Sleep tight

Want a good night's sleep? Follow these steps:
1. Declutter your bedroom.
2. Keep your room cool (60–68°F is ideal).
3. Don't do any work on your bed.
4. Stay off your phone close to bedtime.
5. Avoid caffeine before bedtime.

Eye protection

Certain sports carry the risk of eye injury, so wear suitable eye protection.

337

338

Avoid interrupting your night's sleep with bathroom breaks by not drinking too much before bedtime.

yawn!

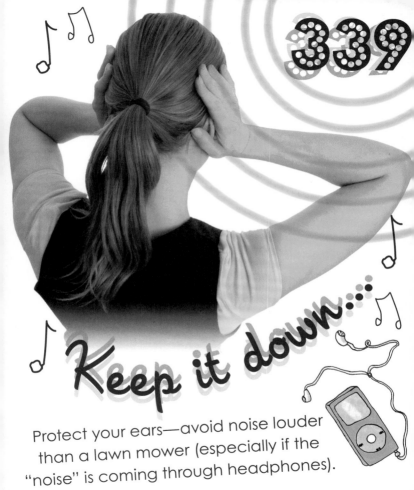

339

Keep it down...

Protect your ears—avoid noise louder than a lawn mower (especially if the "noise" is coming through headphones).

340

Take a risk—if you succeed you'll feel confident; if you don't, you can learn from your mistakes.

Take the plunge

Ditch the sweatpants and brush your hair!

341

spruce up!

Looking good will help you to feel good!

Feeling

343

great

Wear clothes that
flatter your figure,
and you'll feel great
about yourself.

INSPIRE ME

"I have the same goal I've had ever since I was a girl. I want to rule the world."
Madonna

Make an inspiration board. This is a board full of pictures and quotations that inspire you.

x x

Smile! 345

A gorgeous smile radiates inner beauty.

Respect
your friends

346

364 Lifestyle

Treat friends with the respect and consideration you'd like from them.

Go Large

Sunglasses that wrap around offer better side protection for your eyes.

Lifestyle 365

Listen to your body—if you have PMS, you may need more sleep than usual.

And rest ...

348

Be active

Develop your talents—if you enjoy dancing, take up a class. If you're interested in sports, join a team or take lessons.

350

Sleep easy

Don't go to bed hungry or stuffed: Your discomfort may keep you awake.

Weigh it up!

351

Weigh yourself regularly, do it just once a week at the same time, when you are wearing the same clothes.

352

You will lose weight off the parts of your body that you are genetically designed to lose it from.

In your genes ...

Don't let arguments get you down—sort out your differences so you get a good night's rest.

Sort it out 353

If you're worried that you won't be able to sleep, say to yourself, "Tonight, I will sleep well" several times during the day.

354 *Sweet dreams*

355

Know your body, so that if something changes, you'll be able to pick up on it.

Get to know yourself ...

Ease the pain!

Help ease period pains by putting a heat pad on your tummy or lower back.

356

357

Curves are beautiful ...
don't expect to look like a
12-year-old when you're 15.

Curvy curves

358

Staring is good! When using a computer or electronic reading device, rest your eyes by staring into the distance for 20 seconds every 20 minutes.

into space

Try to develop a healthy social life and find some friends you share an interest with.

359

Share with friends

Never share eye makeup or drops with anyone. Eye infections can spread very quickly.

Keep it clean!

361

The Key to life ...

Acceptance is the key.
Learn to love the things
you can't change.

Try new hobbies or sports—you may be surprised at what you're good at.

362

Try new things

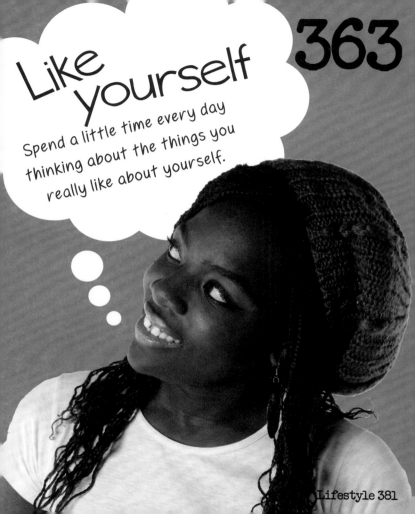

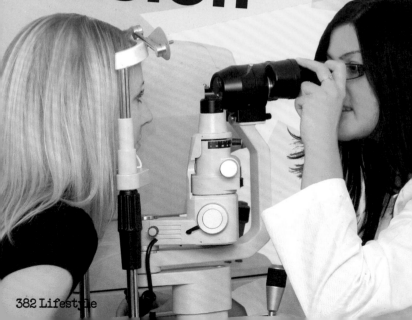

364

Blurry vision

If you're struggling to see, have your eyes tested.